KING ZING'S GONG SONG

Clive Gifford

GW01003552

Illustrated by Andrea Petrlik Huseinovic

King Zing was amazing at writing songs.
People loved to prance and dance
to his best sing-a-longs.
He loved playing them
with his swinging band.
Many people thought his band
was the best in the land.
For two years, King Zing had tried
writing his best ever song.

The song was going well,
but the ending just went wrong!

All year long, King Zing tried out
new sounds to end the song,
but every single sound
turned out to be wrong.

2

Which of these letters can have ing added to the end to make a new word? Write them out.

s _____

c _____

r _____

w _____

f _____

sh _____

sl _____

br _____

3

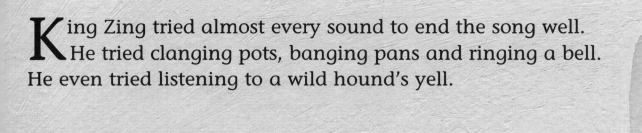

King Zing tried almost every sound to end the song well.
He tried clanging pots, banging pans and ringing a bell.
He even tried listening to a wild hound's yell.

He tried shuffling back and forth
in trays of sand.
He got thirty people to
clap their hands.

He tried pinging the prongs of a fork.
He recorded the sound of the wings of a stork.
He bounced ping-pong balls up and down on a bat.
They were all wrong – and that was that!

4

If you want to add ing to a word ending in the letter e, you usually drop the e. Try adding ing to the following words.

dance _____

write _____

hide _____

prance _____

ride _____

wave _____

bite _____

dive _____

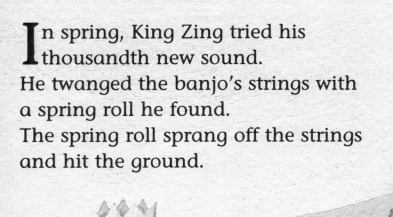

In spring, King Zing tried his thousandth new sound.
He twanged the banjo's strings with a spring roll he found.
The spring roll sprang off the strings and hit the ground.

King Zing wrung his hands and cursed,

"Oh **dung**!"

Just then his doorbell rang, "ding-dong."

In walked King Zing's old friend, Bing.

Bing was fond of King Zing and his swinging singing.
He was upset that King Zing could not find the right thing.

Here are some of the sounds King Zing has tried to use for his song. Can you write the words to match the pictures?

bell   sand   hand claps   pots and pans

fork   ping-pong bats   hound   stork

_____

_____

_____

_____

_____

_____

_____

"Maybe the sound will be found around town," said Bing.

"Oh, Bing, I will try anything!" said King Zing.

In town, King Zing's smile
soon turned into a frown.
Every sound he found was still
wrong for his song.
King Zing then looked up
at a tall building.
On the rooftop he saw
an old, gold gong.
King Zing thought, surely,
he could not be wrong.

This old, gold gong
would be perfect for his song.

All of these words have shorter words hidden inside them. Can you spot the words and write them out?

 zing _____

held _____

pong _____

hold _____

 sung _____

 send _____

fund _____

King Zing climbed up the building to reach the gong. A cold wind blew, biting and strong.

King Zing had to be careful and tried to cling on.

King Zing banged the gong hard. **BONG!**

"Oh dung, the gong's bong
is wrong for my song!"
But that was not all that was wrong.
King Zing's bang on the gong
was too strong. The gong swung!
Into the air he was flung.
He grabbed at the gong
and clung on.

He loved playing them with his swinging band.

He twanged the banjo's strings with a spring roll he found.

 "Oh, Bing, I will try anything!"

He tried clanging pots, banging pans and ringing a bell.

Bing was fond of King Zing and his swinging singing.

"Oh, I wish I had wings," sighed King Zing, looking down.

King Zing's fingers started stinging from clinging on.

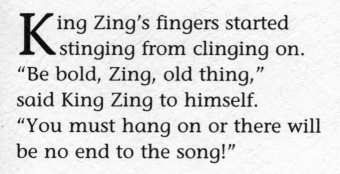

K ing Zing's fingers started
stinging from clinging on.
"Be bold, Zing, old thing,"
said King Zing to himself.
"You must hang on or there will
be no end to the song!"

A crowd gathered on the ground
as fire engine bells rang.

The Fire Chief called up,
"What are you doing, King Zing?"

"Looking for a sound for my song,"
King Zing replied.
"I thought this gong would be grand,
but I was wrong.
Could you help?
I can't hang on for long!"

12

Can you write the four sets of four words which all rhyme, using these words?

cold   mind   hung   find   sung   wrong   rung   sold

clung   told   long   bind   gong   hold   kind   song

_____   _____   _____   _____

_____   _____   _____   _____

_____   _____   _____   _____

_____   _____   _____   _____

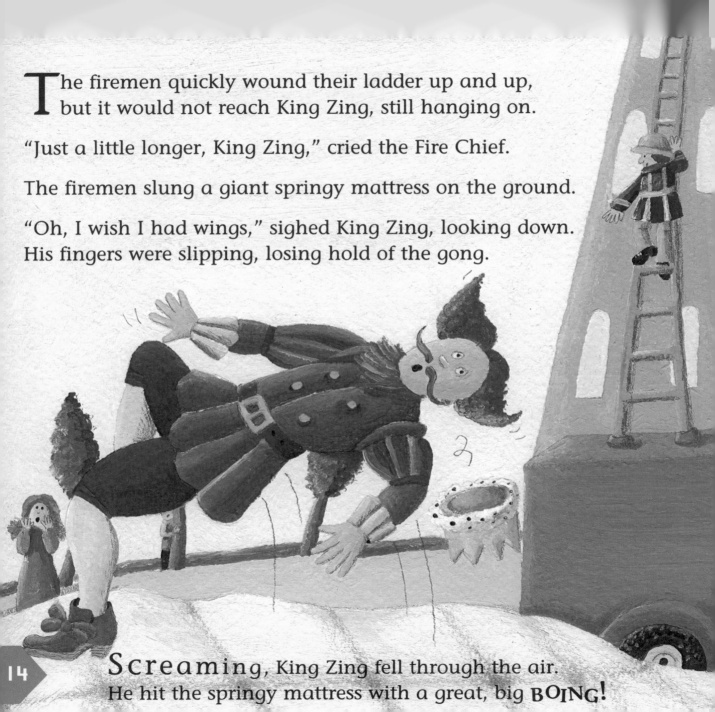

The firemen quickly wound their ladder up and up,
but it would not reach King Zing, still hanging on.

"Just a little longer, King Zing," cried the Fire Chief.

The firemen slung a giant springy mattress on the ground.

"Oh, I wish I had wings," sighed King Zing, looking down.
His fingers were slipping, losing hold of the gong.

Screaming, King Zing fell through the air.
He hit the springy mattress with a great, big BOING!

Can you add either ld or nd to these letters to make new words?

co _____

sa _____

cou _____

sta _____

chi _____

ha _____

spe _____

fu _____

The springs in the mattress were too strong.
The crowd gasped as King Zing was flung back into the air and came down on some dustbins with a giant **CLANG!**

He was covered in stinking rubbish from the bins, but the crowd saw that King Zing had a great big grin.

He thought, "I was wrong about the gold gong! What I needed for my song was on the ground all along. How exciting – I have found the perfect sound!"

Can you sort out these groups of mixed-up letters to spell words from the story?

_____

_____

_____

_____

_____

_____

There was standing room only at the Grand Hall.
King Zing would be playing his new song for the City Ball.
The curtains swung open and there was King Zing's band.

To one side of the band
stood a very high stand.
It was made from lots of poles
strung together with thick string.
On the top of the stand
stood King Zing's friend, Bing.

King Zing bowed, then turned to his band.
With a wave of his hand, his new song began.

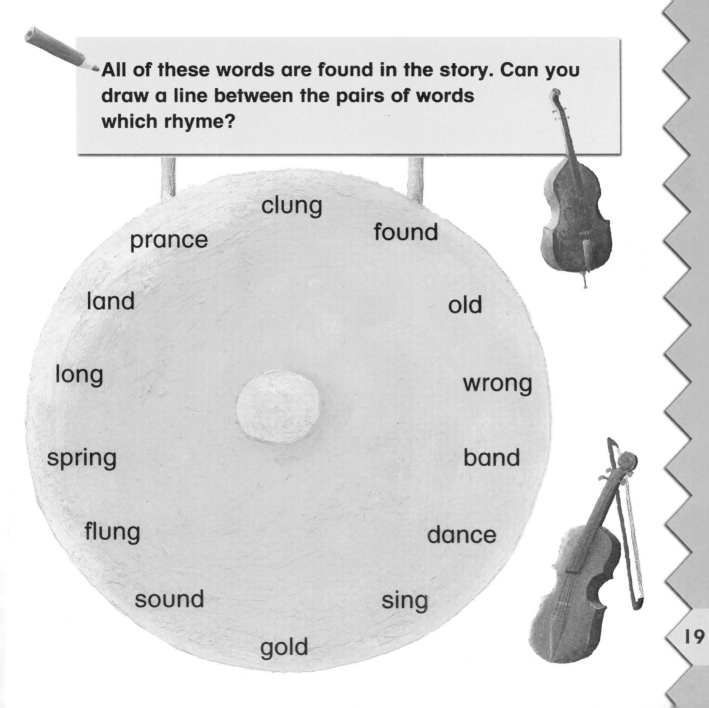

All of these words are found in the story. Can you draw a line between the pairs of words which rhyme?

clung

prance

found

land

old

long

wrong

spring

band

flung

dance

sound

sing

gold

First, some drums banged and the string section twanged.
Then lots of bells rang as the band sang.
The crowd loved the song and began to sing along.

"Here comes the ending," smiled
King Zing, looking up at Bing.

Bing sprang off the stand,
landing on a giant spring.

The spring flung Bing
across the stage
into some dustbins.

CLANG!

The crowd went wild, as Bing took a bow with King Zing.
It was a clang, not a bong, the song had needed all along.

Now you have read the story, try to answer these questions about King Zing and his Gong Song.

1. How long had King Zing been trying to write his best song? _____

2. What type of balls had King Zing bounced up and down? _____

3. What did King Zing use to play his banjo? _____

4. What colour was the old gong that King Zing climbed up to reach? _____

5. What did King Zing crash into with a clang? _____

6. Who stood on top of the stand at the concert? _____

Answers

Page 3

sing
ring
wing
sling
bring

Page 5

dancing
writing
hiding
prancing
riding
waving
biting
diving

Page 7

hand claps

fork

stork

ping-pong
bats

hound

pots and
pans

bell

sand

Page 9

zing → in   sung → sun
held → he   send → end
pong → on   fund → fun
hold → old

Page 11

He loved (playing) them with his (swinging) band.

He twanged the banjo's (strings) with a (spring) roll he found.

"Oh, (Bing,) I will try (anything)"

He tried (clanging) pots, (banging) pans and (ringing) a bell.

(Bing) was fond of (King) (Zing) and his (swinging) (singing)

"Oh, I wish I had (wings)" sighed (King) (Zing) (looking) down.

(King) (Zing's) fingers started (stinging) from (clinging) on.

Page 13

cold sold told hold

mind find bind kind

hung sung rung clung

wrong long gong song

Page 15

cold, sand, could, stand, child, hand, spend, fund

Page 17

gong	songs
banjo	hound
bins	spring
ladder	building

Page 19

clung – flung

found – sound

old – gold

wrong – long

band – land

dance – prance

sing – spring

Page 21

1. two years
2. ping-pong balls
3. a spring roll
4. gold
5. dustbins
6. Bing

Published 2005

Letts Educational, The Chiswick Centre,
414 Chiswick High Road, London W4 5TF
Tel 020 8996 3333   Fax 020 8996 8390
Email mail@lettsed.co.uk
www.letts-education.com

Text, design and illustrations © Letts Educational Ltd 2005

Book Concept, Development and Series Editor:
Helen Jacobs, Publishing Director
Author: Clive Gifford
Book Design: 2idesign Ltd, Cambridge
Illustrations: Andrea Petrlik Huseinovic, The Bright Agency

Letts Educational Limited is a division of Granada Learning.
Part of Granada plc.

British Library Cataloguing in Publication Data

A CIP record for this book is available from the British Library.

ISBN 1 84315 487 0

Printed in Italy

Colour reproduction by PDQ Digital Media Solutions Ltd, Bungay,
Suffolk NR35 1BY